Introduction

From the earliest times, human beings have looked up to the stars for inspiration and enlightenment. It's easy to see why. Somehow, simply by staring up into the night sky, we feel awe for the great mystery of life and feel ourselves opened up to another way of experiencing reality. We feel transported.

The human fascination with the mysteries of the universe inspired the ancients to study the wondrous patterns and arrangements of the stars, or constellations. After a time, as people became more familiar with this great canopy, they gave names to the constellations based on their own religious or mythological beliefs. Names by which we still know them today.

It is with this same drive for penetrating life's mysteries—particularly the mystery of three-dimensionality—that scientists and artists today are beginning to show us how we can look at a certain flat two-dimensional image and learn to see it—with our own eyes—in three dimensions. Through the advances made possible by computer-generated art and imagery, we can experience that same sense of transport into the night sky, through a new way of looking.

When you flip through the pages of *3-D Galaxy*, you will see images which, when you first look at each of them, will seem like a chaotic jumble of dots onto which a familiar star constellation has been superimposed. These images will seem flat and two-dimensional. They are not. Each of these pictures has the potential to become three-dimensional, revealing another image hidden behind the stars.

These images are called stereograms, and when properly viewed with the naked eye, they will take you on a thrilling flight into a three-dimensional "other space." When you arrive there you will see Sagittarius, the Archer; Andromeda, the Chained Lady; Auriga, the Charioteer, as the ancients must have imagined them. You will see the changing constellations of the night sky as they appear during each of the four seasons. And you will see them all through the power of your own eyes and mind.

How to See in 3-D

When you see the three-dimensional image in a stereogram you are "seeing" in a whole new way. You will be tempted to look at the random-dot image on each page of this book in *search* of the hidden picture. This is the way you normally "look." But with a stereogram you don't look *at* or *for* anything; instead you let your eyes take on a vacant, passive stare through the page. Your brain will do the work of putting together the three-dimensional image.

As with meditation or any activity in which you become so totally focused that you experience reality in a slightly different way, when you relax and begin to see the hidden image rise up from the stereogram, you feel as though you have "clicked" into a new awareness.

Discovering the three-dimensional image in a stereogram may seem difficult, but it's not. All you need is a little patience, a little quiet time, and some simple techniques.

Three-dimensional perception is based on the fact that human beings see with two eyes. Though each eye sees something different, our brain looks for what the two images have in common and puts them together into one three-dimensional whole. The stereogram, which is produced by computer, is designed so that it offers each eye slightly different view of the same thing. Our eyes will naturally put the two views together—provided we look at the stereogram in the right way.

Technique #1 Prepare yourself by relaxing. Understand that you will not be looking *for* the hidden image, but that it will come to you out of the random-dot background.

At first you will see only a blurry image. Allow your eyes to relax. Raise the picture to eye level and bring it your face as close as your nose. With your eyes parallel stare past the image to some invisible place in the distance. Keeping your eyes relaxed, continue to stare through the image as you very gradually pull the book away from your nose. Do it very *slowly* so that you don't disrupt your gaze. Again, don't look *for* anything . . . it will come.

Continue pulling the book away. Once you are fully relaxed, your eyes will start to focus in a new way—that will feel as if something has clicked in—and you will begin to see the blur disappear as the hidden image takes shape. You will be tempted to look *for* it. Don't. (If you do slip and start to look for the image on the page, start over.) Once you *do* see the hidden image fully, it will seem as though you are looking into an entirely new three-dimensional plane both above and below the picture. Your eyes can then freely roam around these newly revealed picture planes until you break your focus.

It's a meditative, relaxing, and eye-opening experience.

Technique #2 Another way to find the images in a stereogram is to cross your eyes. Again, relax. Pick any point on the picture. Increase your focus by allowing your eyes to cross. In a few moments, as you begin to uncross your eyes, the hidden image will leap from the page. It may take a few attempts before this technique clicks for you. Don't be discouraged. Just remember to relax your eyes and be patient.

Technique #3 If you are still having a hard time getting started, try focusing on the cover image. Since the cover has a glossy surface, you can use the reflection to concentrate your eyes on something other than the image. You needn't think about parallel or cross-eye viewing. Bring the book up to your nose, as suggested in the first technique above, and continue from there to relax your eyes on the reflected surface and move the picture away from your face.

After practice, using any of these simple approaches, you will become a master. The Zen masters knew the rewards of seeing in a new way and the feeling of calm it brings. When relaxed and focused, our mind has a natural tendency toward order—psychologists call it Gestalt. Spiritualists called it enlightenment. You'll call it exciting and fun. And you will have a new view of the constellations and a new appreciation for the power of your own mind.

3-D GALAXY

SEE THE HIDDEN PICTURES IN THE STARS

Spring

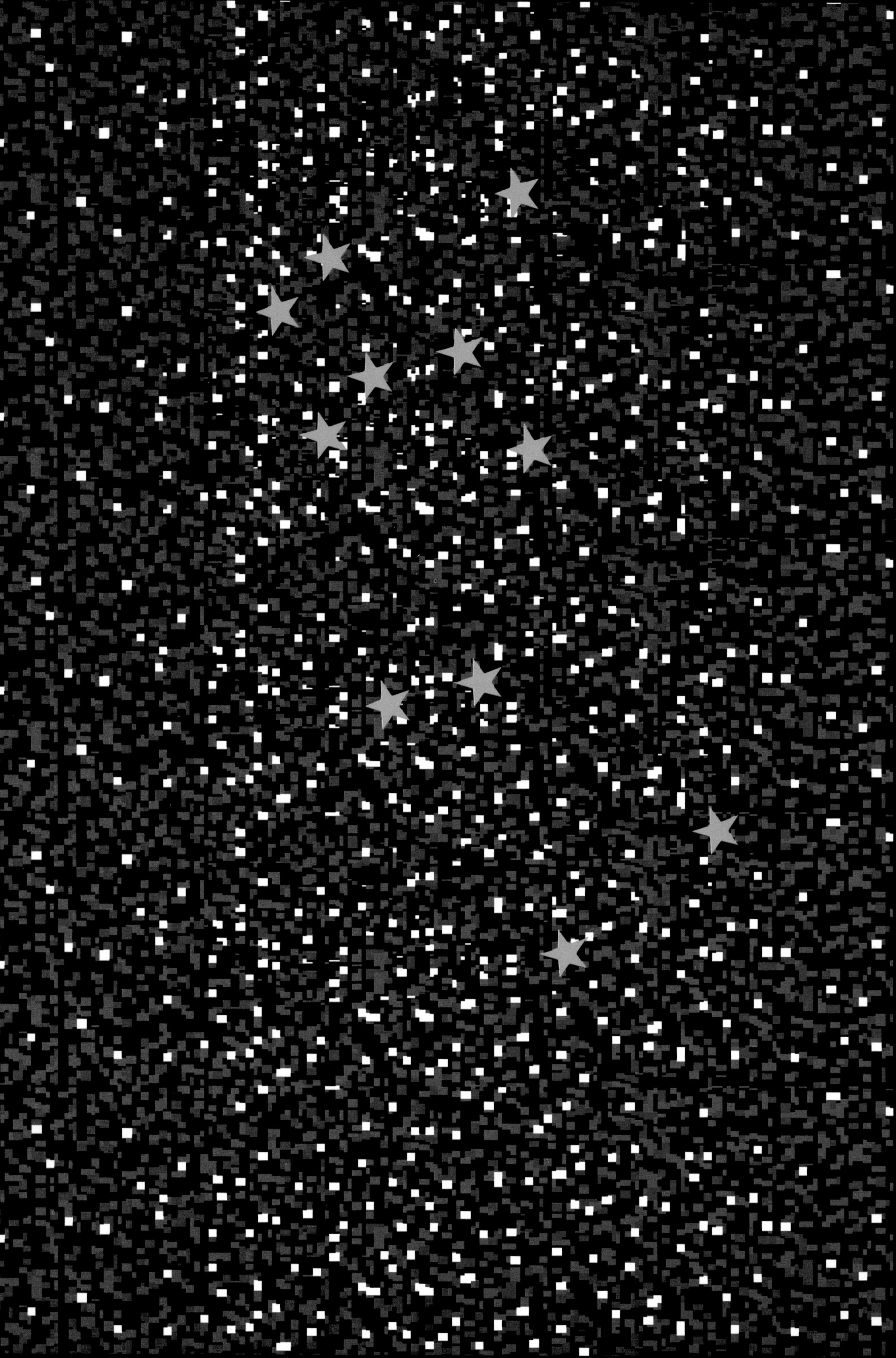

Leo • The Lion

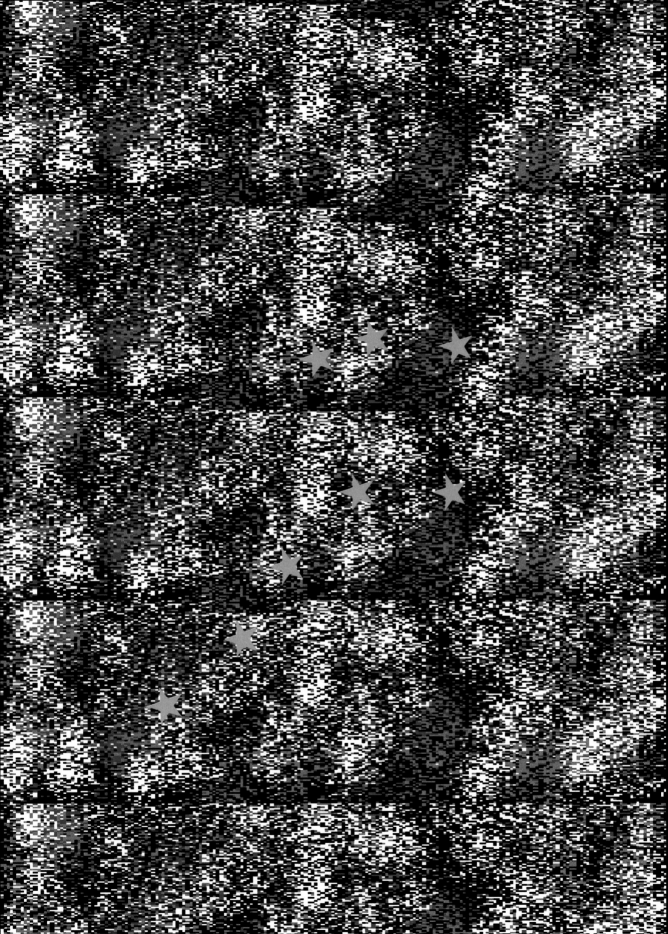

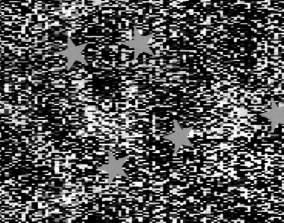
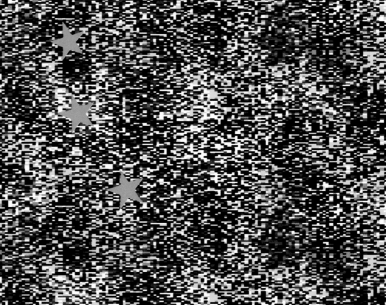

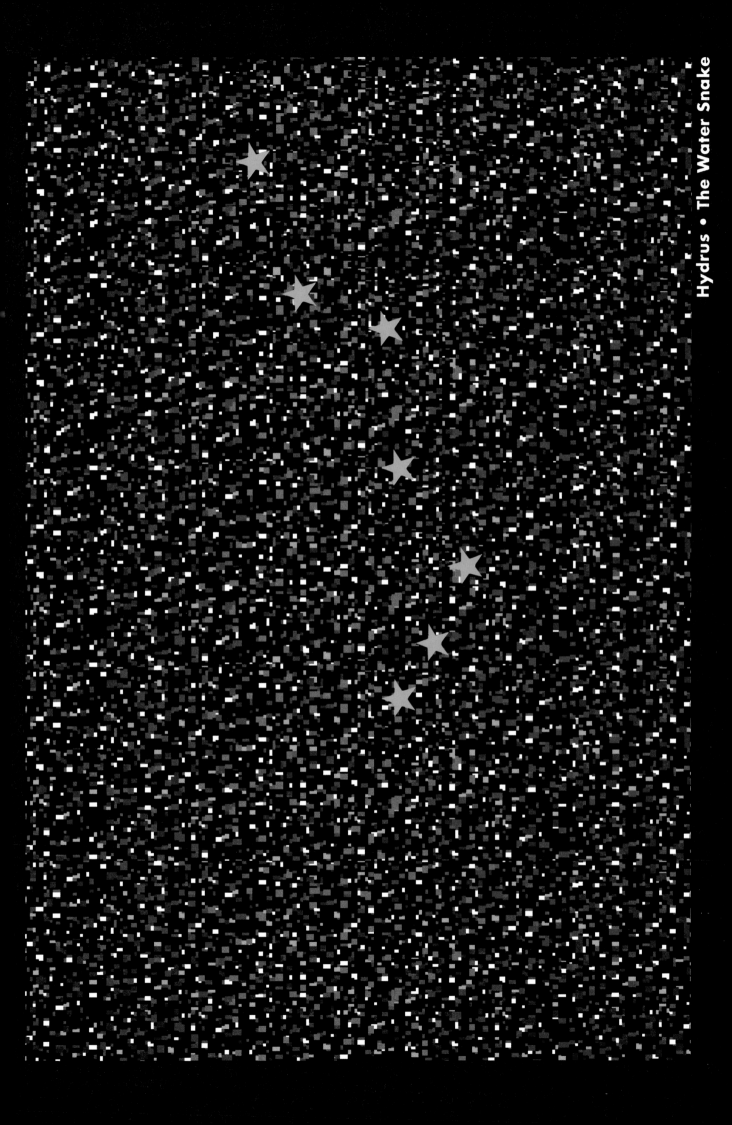

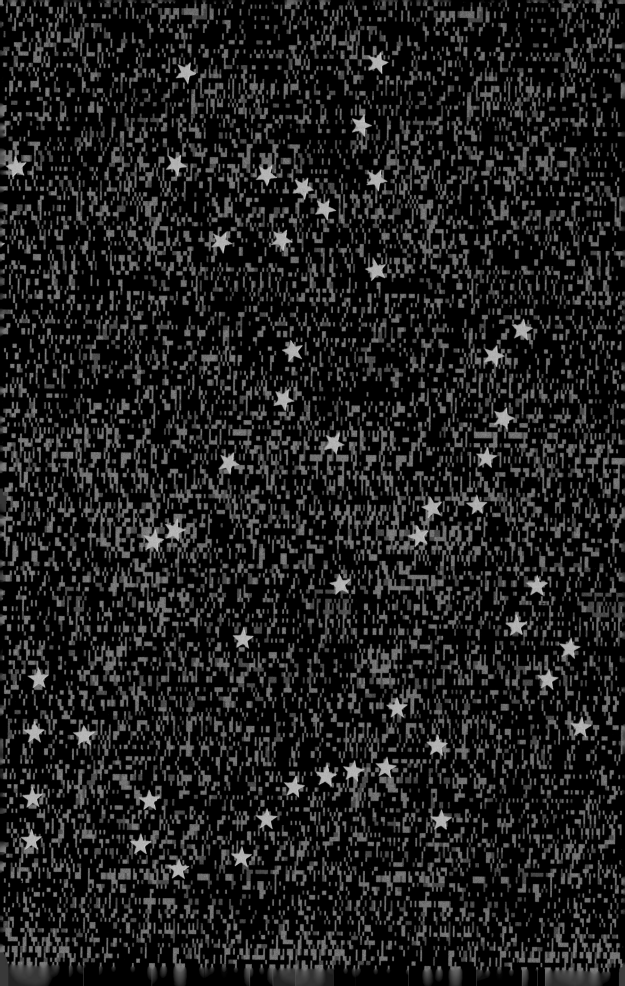

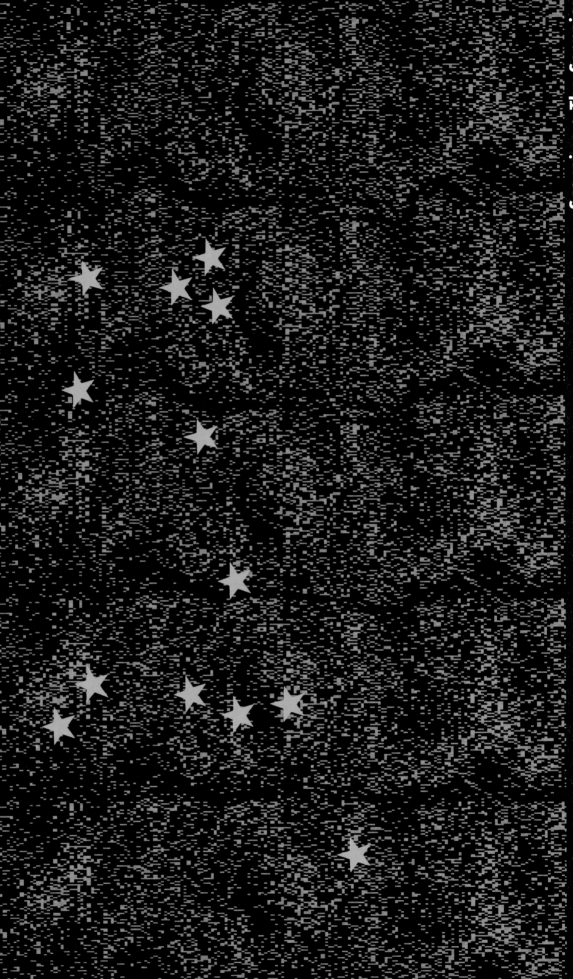

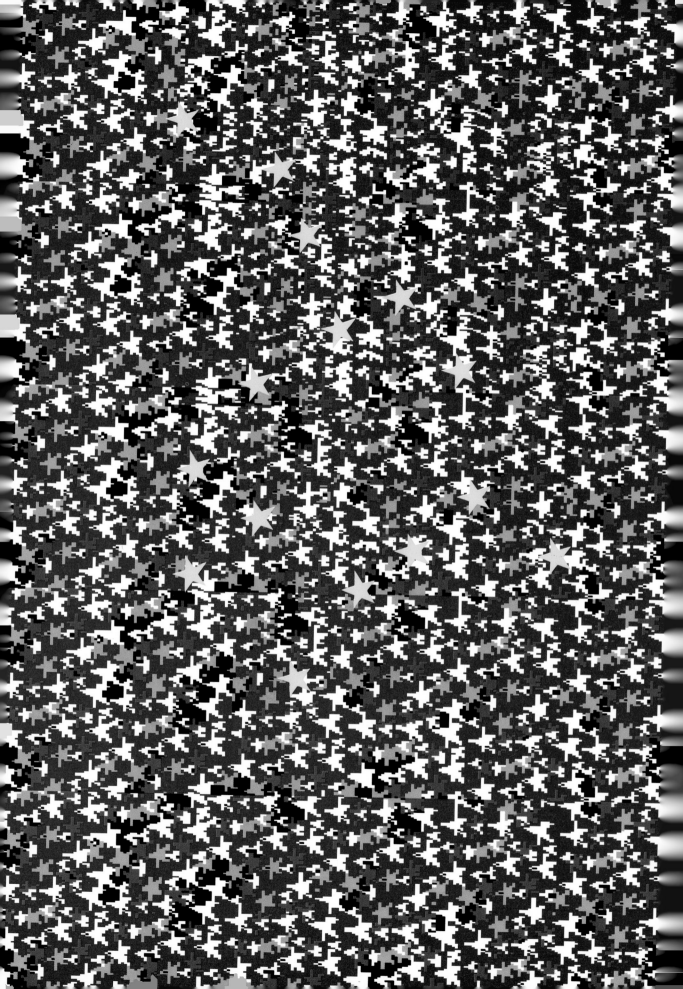

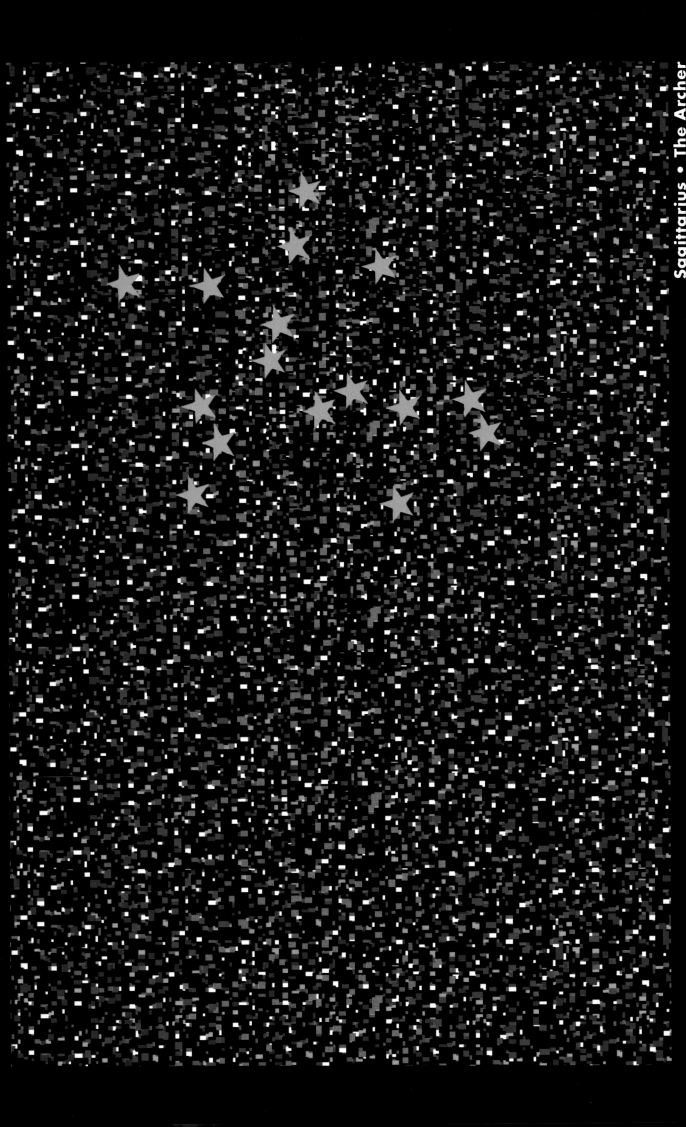

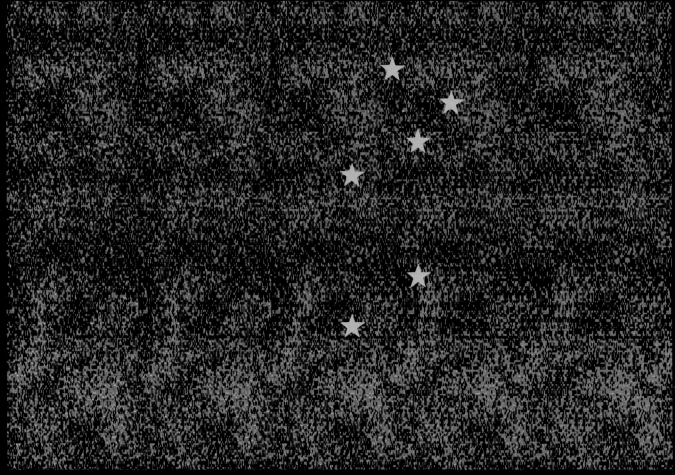

Lyra • The Lyre

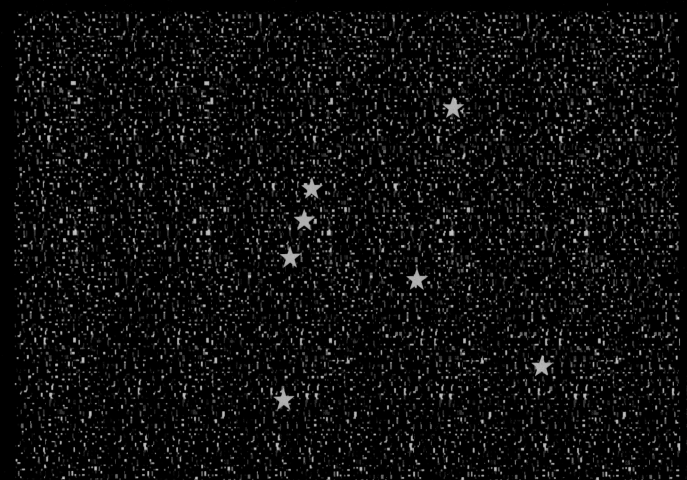

Aquila • The Eagle

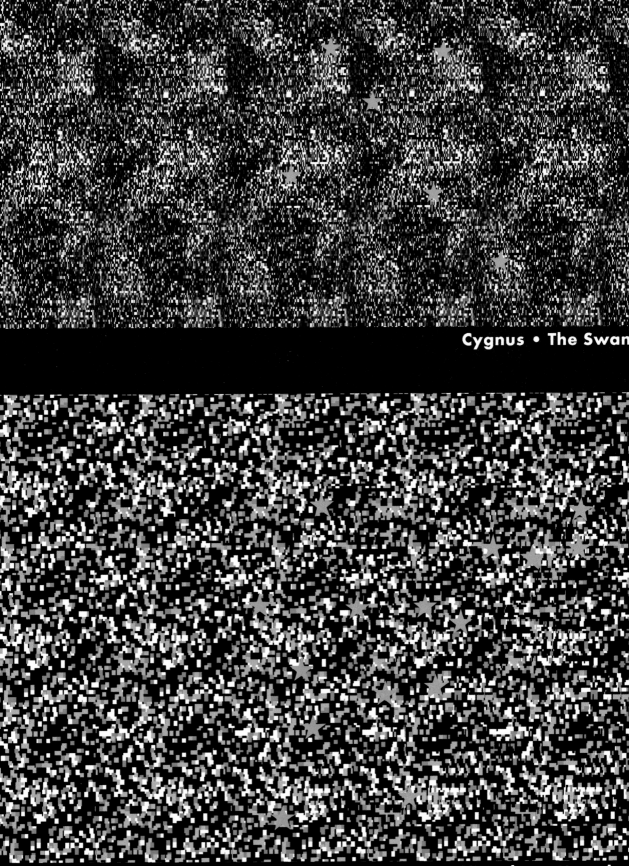

Cygnus • The Swan

Hercules • Hercules

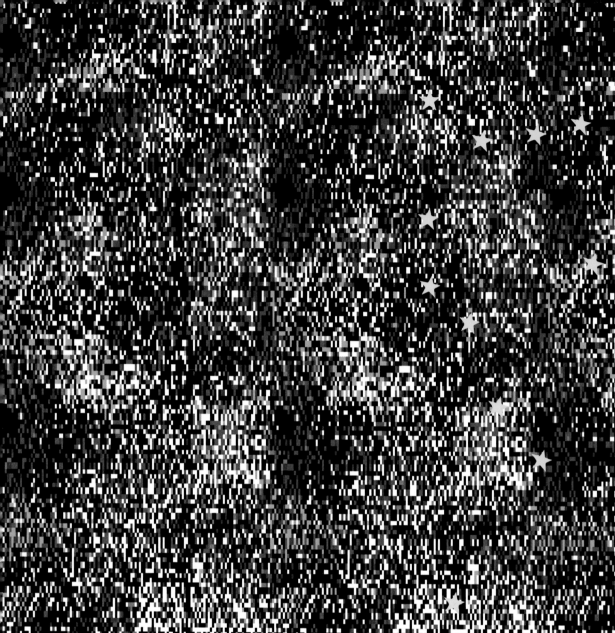

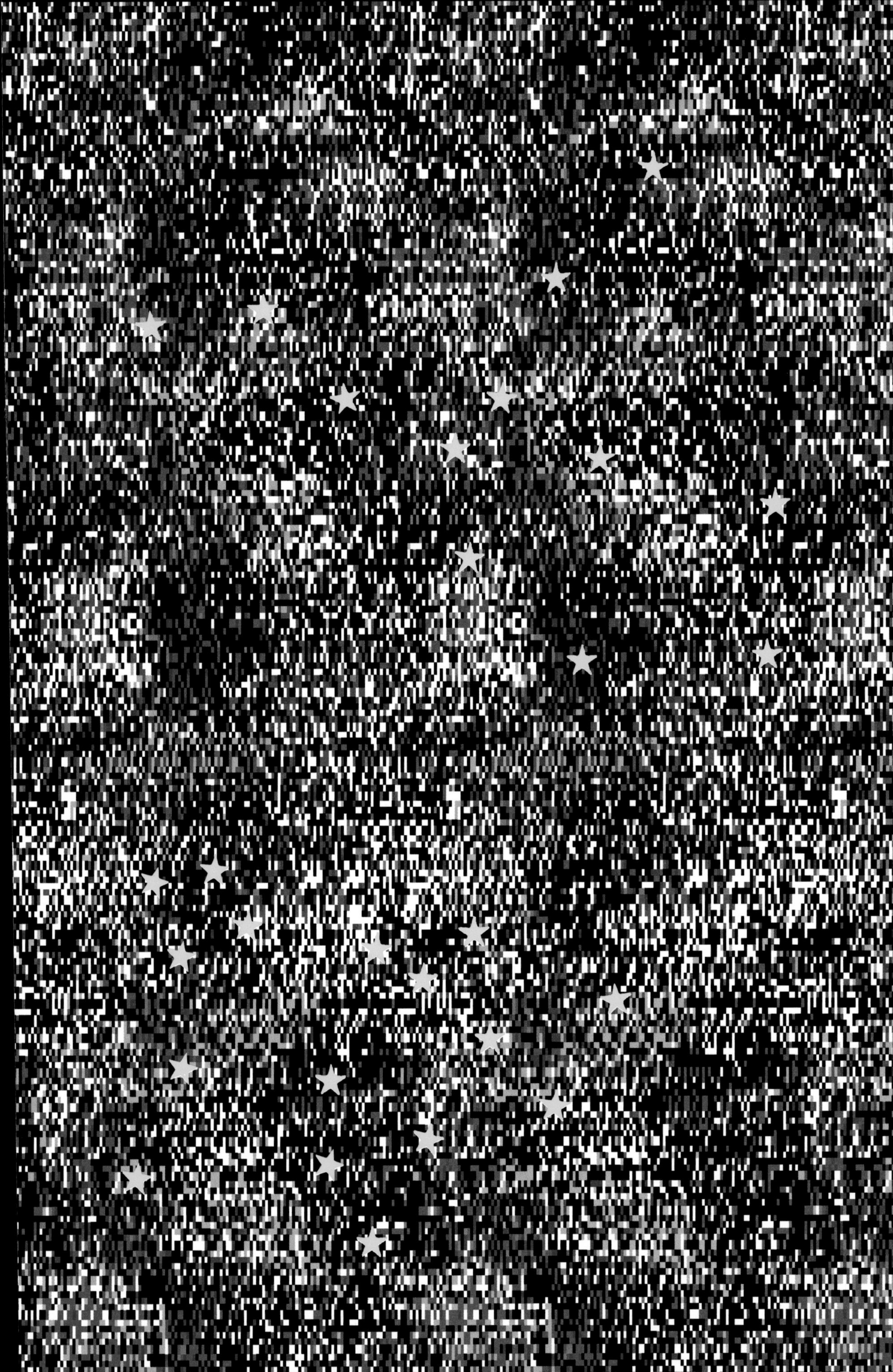

Autumn

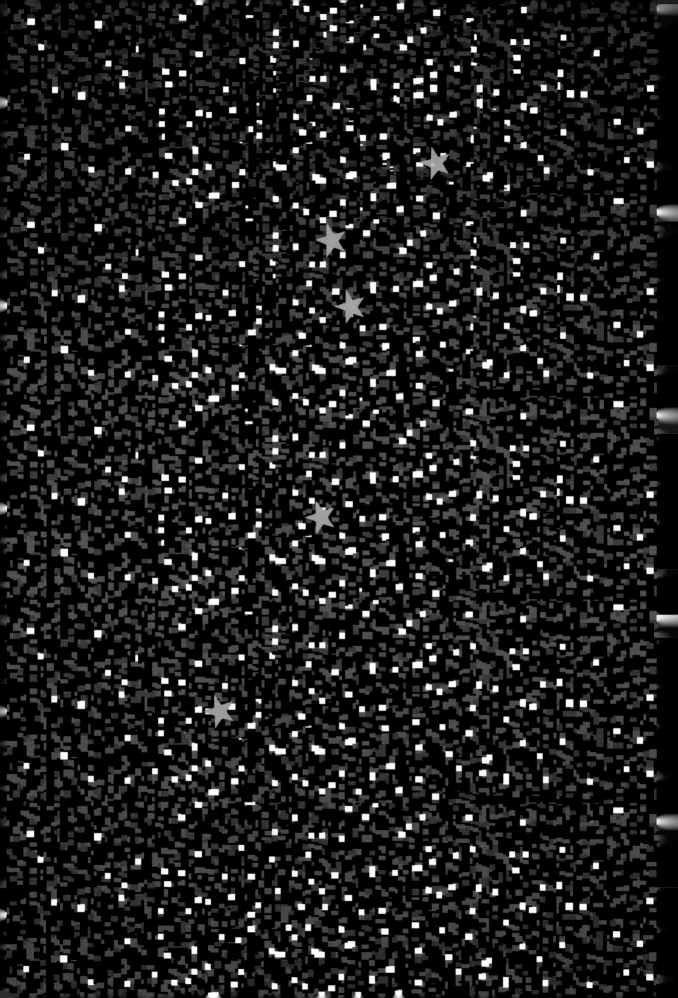

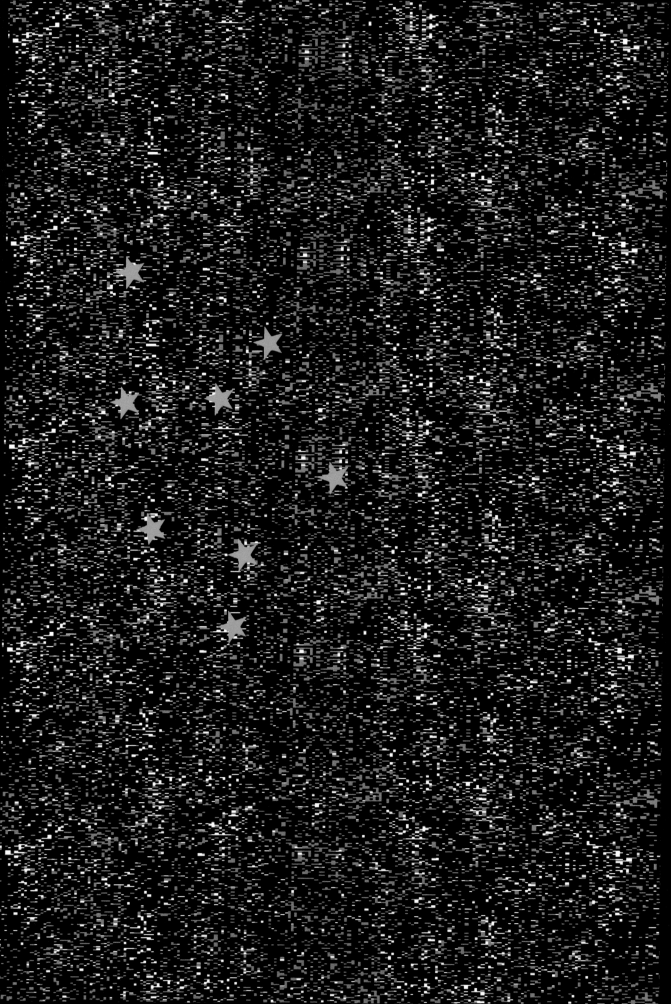

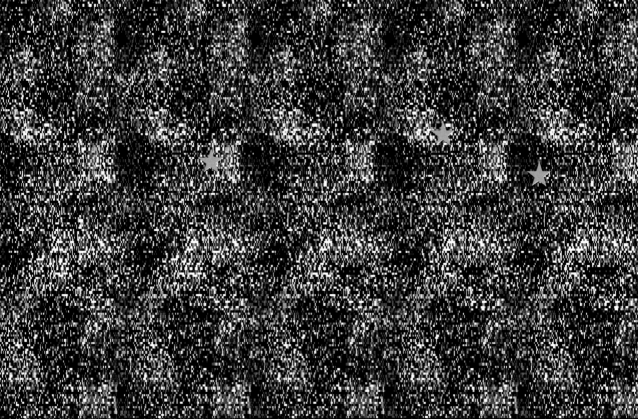

Pisces • The Fishes

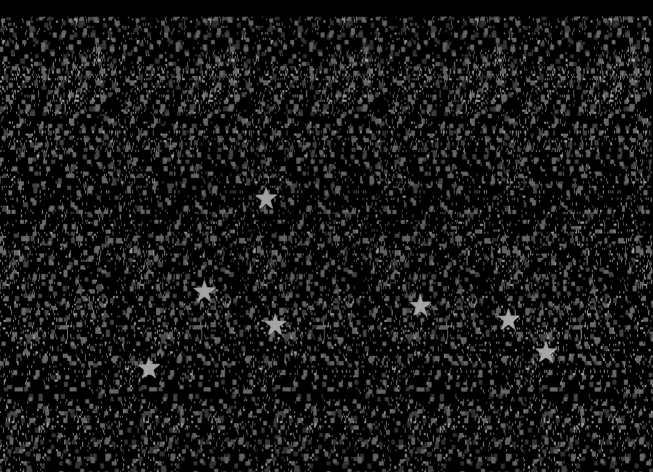

Aries • The Ram

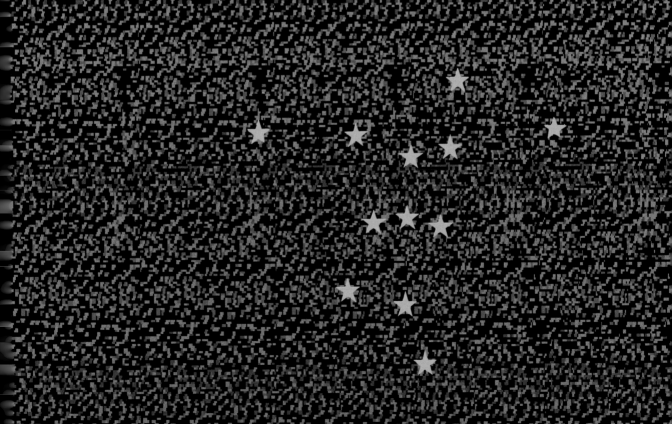

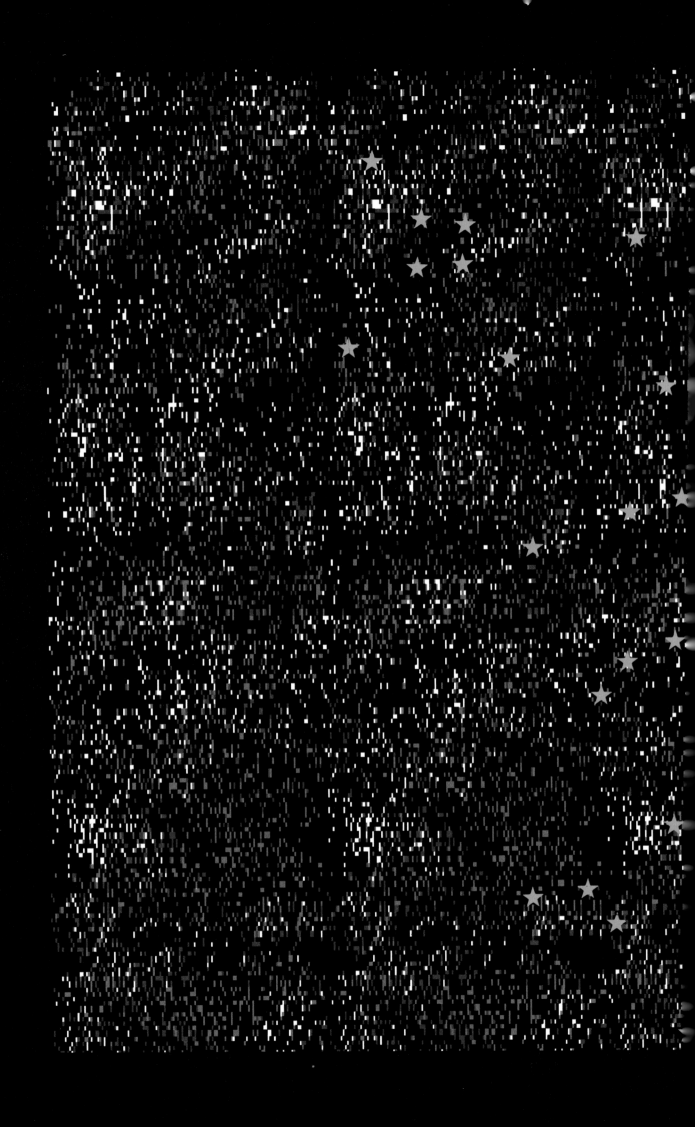

Winter

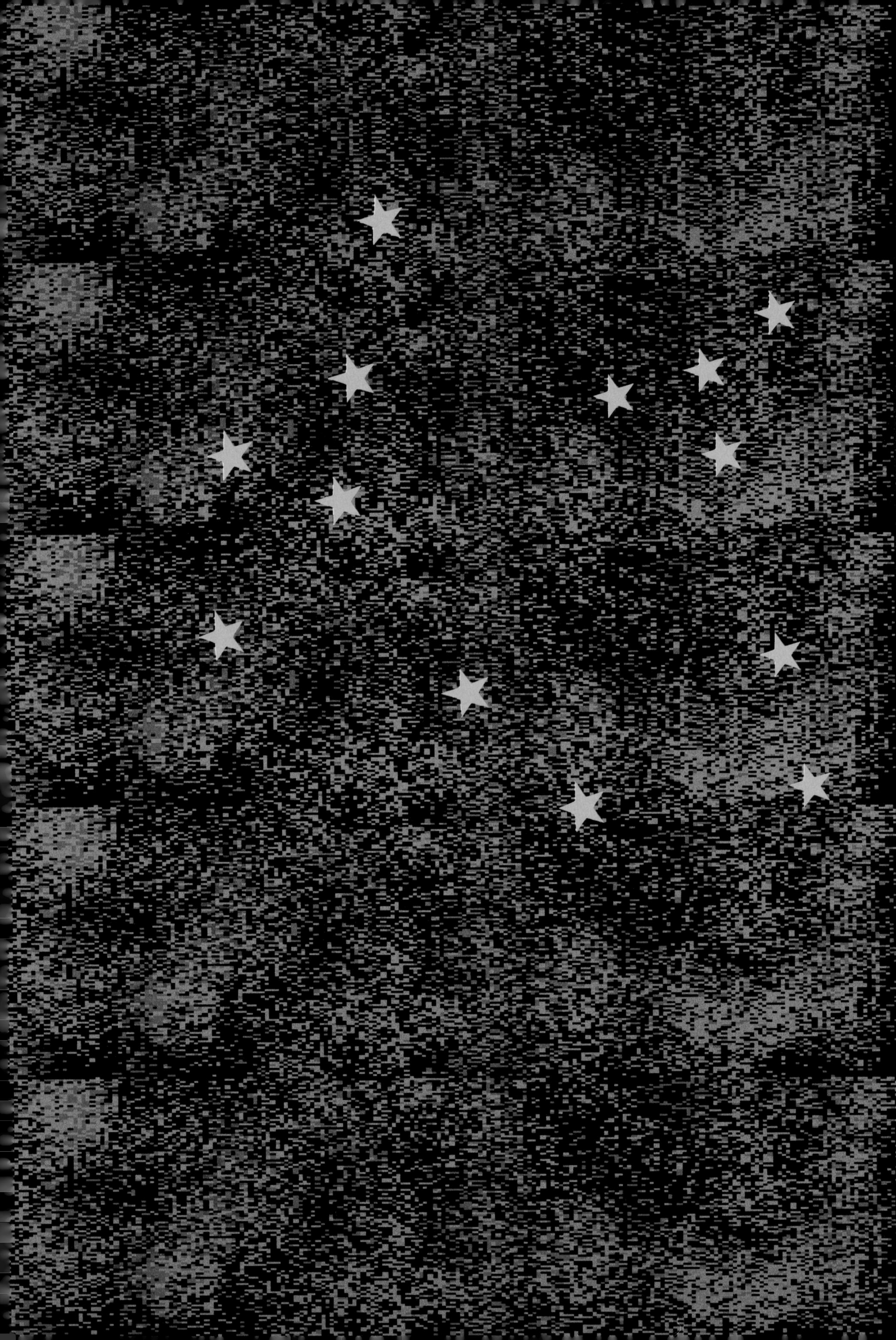

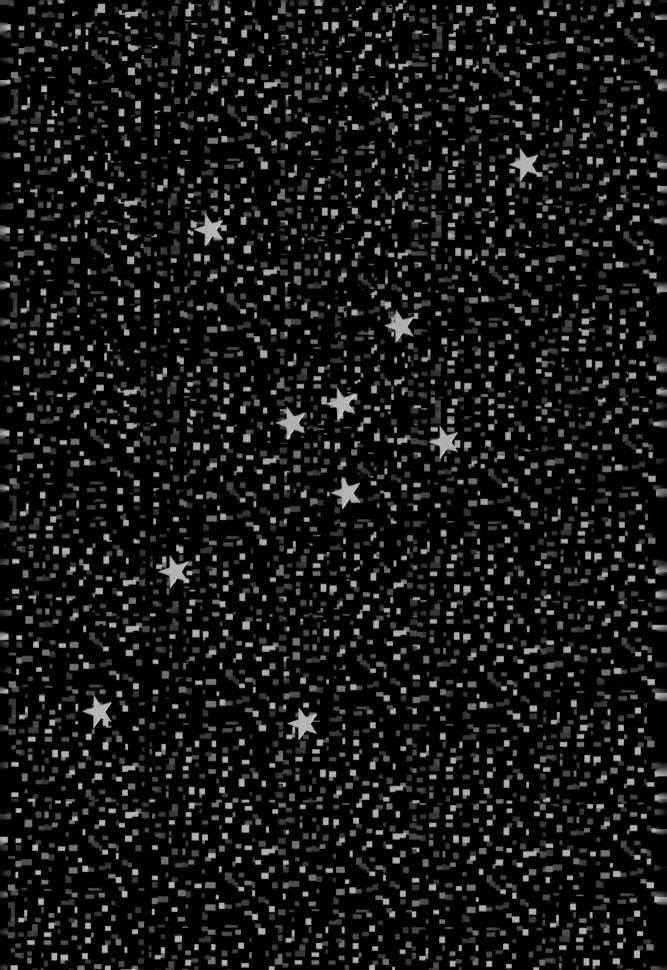

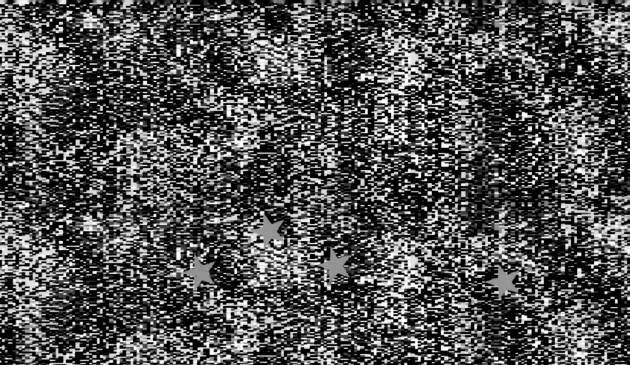

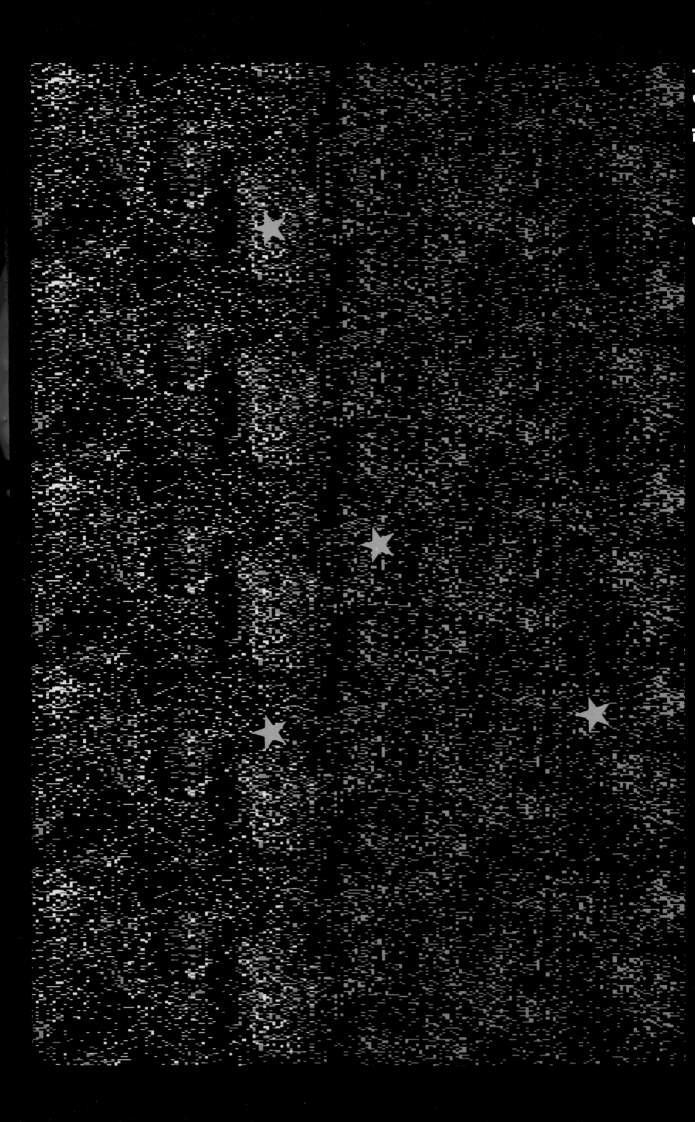

Canis Major • The Larger Dog

Canis Minor • The Smaller Dog

Monoceros • The Unicorn

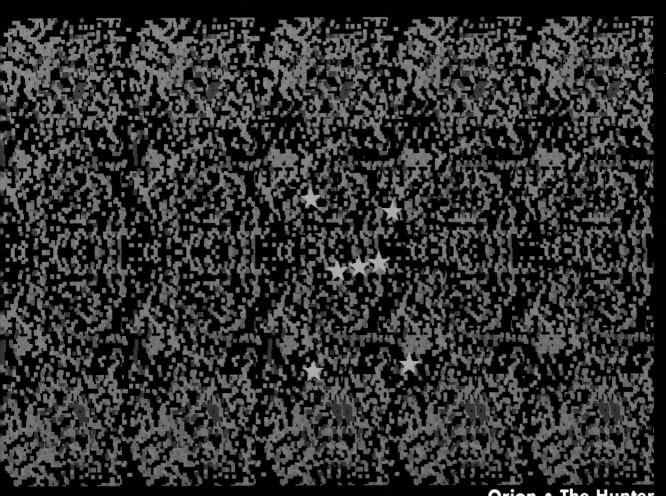

Orion • The Hunter

3-D Galaxy : See the Hidden Pictures in the Stars

ISBN 0688-14018-1

Printed in the United States of America

First Edition

1 2 3 4 5 6 7 8 9 10

3-D GALAXY

Spring

Summer

Autumn

Winter

What You See in 3-D

Ursa Minor

Libra

Aquarius

Taurus

Orion

Crater

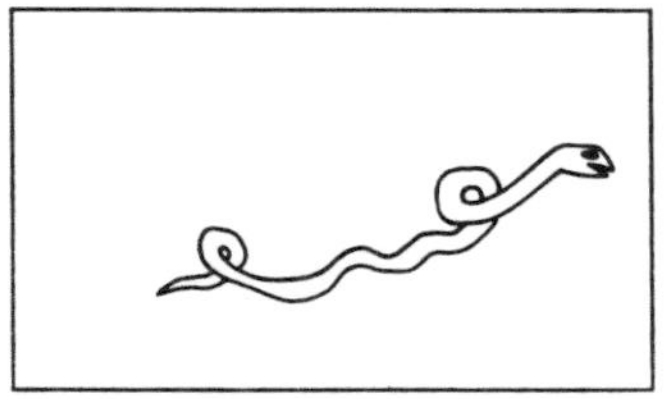

Sagittarius

Cetus

Gemini

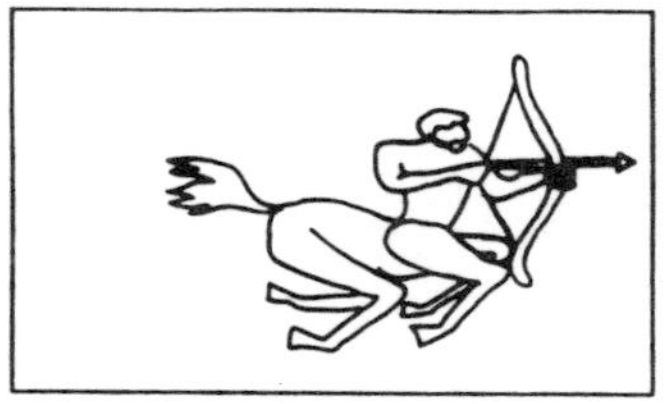

Monoceros

Boötes

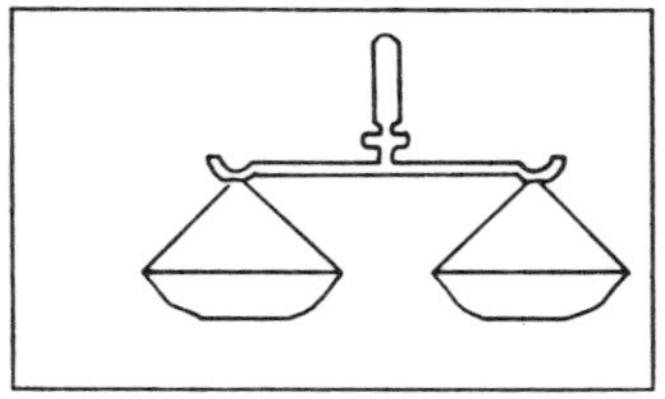

Ophiuchus

Hercules

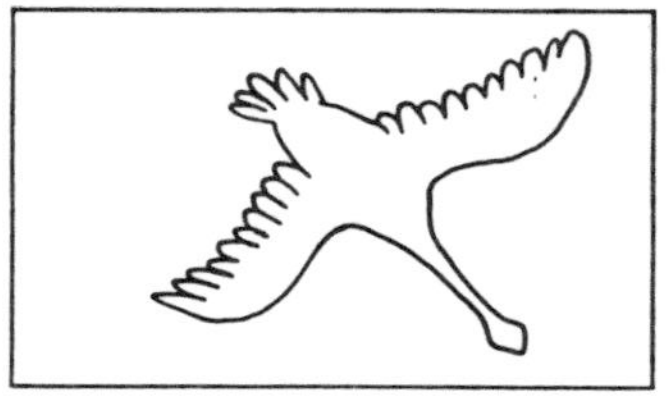

Andromeda

Canis Minor

Leo

Scorpius

Cygnus

Perseus

Canis Major

Virgo

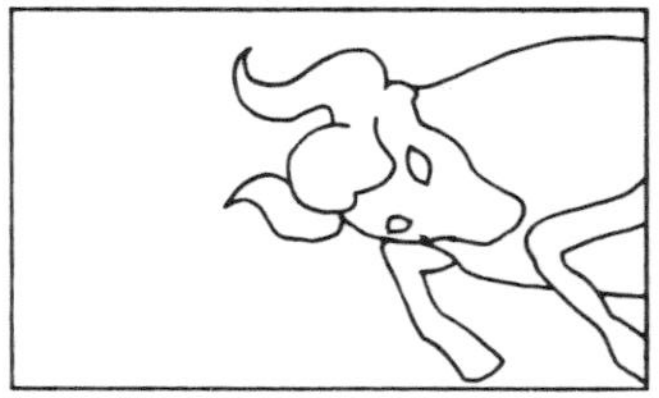

Hydrus

Aquila

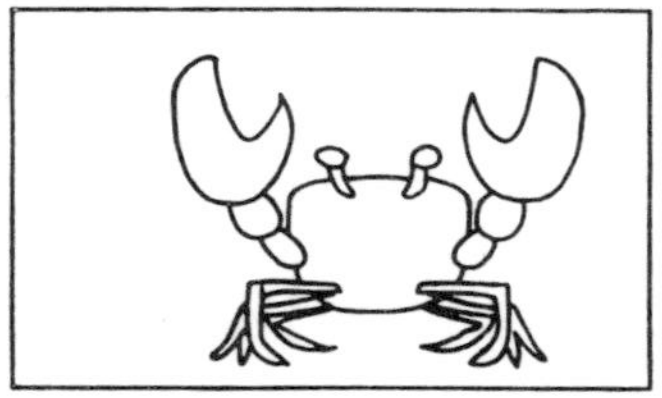

Aries

Cancer

Ursa Major

Lyra

Pisces

Auriga